IN SCOTLAND

This book belongs to:

SCOTLAND (SOUTH)

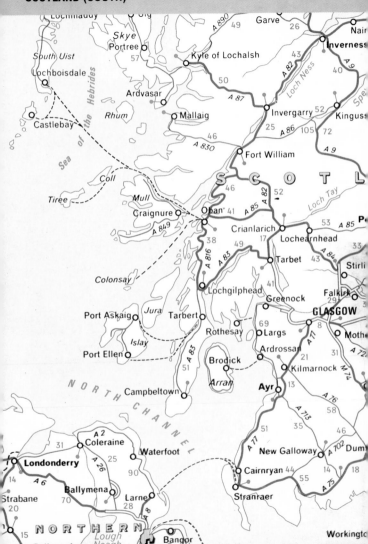

SCOTLAND (NORTH)

Unst

Yell

SHETLAND ISLANDS

Whalsay

Mainland

Scalloway Lerwick

Kirkwall *Aberdeen*

St

ORKNEY ISLAN

Durness

27 A 836

31 Tongue

A 856 39

A 897

Stornoway

Lewis

72 Loch Shin

B

THE MINCH

Tarbert Ullapool

89

North Uist 31 A 835

Lochmaddy Uig A 890 49 Garve 26 A 9

Skye Na

Portree Inverness

South Uist 57 Kyle of Lochalsh 43 Loch Ness 40

Lochboisdale 50 A 82 Spe

Ardvasar A 87 Invergarry 52 Kingus

Sea of the Hebrides *Rhum* 25 A 86 105 72

Castlebay Mallaig 46 A 9

A 830 Fort William

Coll 46 S C O T L

Tiree *Mull* A 82 52 Loch Tay

Westray

Pousay

Sanday

Stronsay

nland

Kirkwall

Scalloway

oy

urso

92

Wick

58

Elgin   35   Banff   Fraserburgh

17   21   A 98

Keith

64   A 96   51   68

Lerwick

A 93   ABERDEEN

Dee   59   A 92

Braemar   Stonehaven

67   A 94   68

N   D

A 92

DUNDEE

Bruce's Stone

Bruce's Stone in Galloway
Forest Park is in memory of the
victory over the English by
Robert Bruce (1274-1329) and
his followers at this site in 1307.
The Park is a splendid wild land
covering more than 240 square
miles (620 sq km) including the
range known as the Rhinns of
Kells.

I-Spy for 25

Burns' Statue, Dumfries

Ellisland Farm was a failure for
Robert Burns, and he moved to
'Queen of the South', Dumfries, the
market town where he was born and
where his statue now stands. In
which year did he move here?

I-Spy for 20
Double with answer

Thomas Carlyle's Birthplace

Thomas Carlyle (1795-1881),
the writer and historian, was
born the son of a stonemason
here in Ecclefechan. Carlyle
died in London but was buried
in his home town. Two master
masons built this house. Who
were they?

I-Spy for 20 — double with answer

Craigleuth Collection

A baronial stone mansion, 2 miles from Langholm among the Eskdale Hills, houses the Craigleuth Collection of tribal artifacts. From which countries do the artifacts come?

I-Spy for **20**
Double with answer

Ellisland Farm

Ellisland Farm, to the north-west of Dumfries, was once leased by Scotland's national poet, Robert Burns (1759-96). It was here that he wrote 'Auld Lang Syne'.
I-Spy for **15**

Kirkcudbright

In the far distance is the royal burgh of Kirkcudbright, one of the oldest towns in Scotland. It stands close to the estuary of the River Dee. Who was the pirate who troubled the town in the 1570s?

I-Spy for **20**
Double with answer

Maxwelton House

The seventeenth-century Maxwelton House, north-west of Dumfries, is the stronghold of the Earls of Glencairn. It was also the birthplace of Annie Laurie, the lass immortalized in song. When was she born?

Maclellan's Castle

Dominating the harbour of Kirkcudbright stands the immense sixteenth-century ruin of Maclellan's Castle, built by Sir Thomas Maclellan.
I-Spy for 15

I-Spy for 10
Double with answer

Museum of Costume

The Museum of Costume is to be found in New Abbey, 8 miles south of Dumfries. What is the name of the famous abbey which is nearby?

I-Spy for 20
Double with answer

Abbotsford House
The Scottish novelist and poet, Sir Walter Scott (1771-1832), bought Abbotsford House in Roxburgh in 1811, and it remained his home until his death. What was the house called when Sir Walter bought it, and what does the name mean?

I-Spy for **10**
Double with answer

Abbotsford's Gardens
Sir Walter Scott was the most popular writer of Scottish ballads and historical novels of his day, but he was also a collector. He acquired something which once belonged to the Scottish outlaw, Rob Roy (1671-1734). What was it?

I-Spy for **20** — *double with answer*

Coldstream Guards Memorial
Coldstream is located at the site of the first dependable crossing of the River Tweed upstream of Berwick. The Coldstream Guards, part of the Household Brigade, were founded here in 1660.
I-Spy for **20**

9

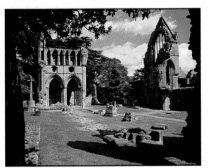

Dryburgh Abbey

Dryburgh Abbey is situated to the south-east of the quiet Borders town of Melrose. It was founded in the twelfth century when David was king of Scotland. Like other Borders abbeys, it was burned down by the Earl of Hertford in 1545 during the reign of Henry VIII.

I-Spy for **20**

Edin's Hall Broch

Edin's Hall Broch, to the north of Duns, was occupied during the first and third centuries. It is 90 feet (27.4 m) in diameter and its walls, which contain rooms or cells, are 19 feet (5.8 m) thick. What is a broch?

I-Spy for **15**
Double with answer

Hermitage Castle

Just off the B6399 road about 16 miles to the south of Hawick are the imposing remains of the thirteenth-century Hermitage Castle. It belonged in turn to the families of de Soulis and then Douglas, and has a macabre history of murders.

I-Spy for **15**

Jedburgh Abbey

Jedburgh Abbey, overlooking the River Jed, was founded by David I of Scotland in 1138 as an Augustinian Priory. Completed in 1227, how many times was it burned before being left in ruins by Henry VIII?

I-Spy for 15
Double with answer

Mary Queen of Scots' House

Not far from the abbey at Jedburgh is the house of Mary Stuart (1542-87) who was beheaded for plotting to murder Elizabeth I of England, her cousin. Among the relics to be seen there is a death mask of Mary.

I-Spy for 15

Melrose

Melrose is famous for its ruined twelfth-century abbey, rebuilt by Robert the Bruce (1274-1329), but it is the annual June Festival which turns this quiet Borders town into one of Scotland's biggest tourist attractions.

I-Spy for 15

Thirlstane Castle
Thirlstane Castle, near Lauder, was built as a fort but, in the sixteenth century, it became a dwelling house. The castle is built of pink sandstone, and it houses a collection of furniture and paintings.
I-Spy for **20**

St Abb's Head
The rocky promontory of St Abb's Head to the north of St Abbs forms part of the 77-hectare (192-acre) National Nature Reserve established in 1980. It is south-east Scotland's most important area for cliff-nesting birds, and colonies of fulmars, guillemots, razorbills, and kittiwakes abound.
I-Spy for **20**

Wilton Lodge Park
To the west of the town of Hawick is Wilton Lodge Park, the ancestral home of the Langland family. It now houses Hawick Museum and Art Gallery where there is a large collection of Borders relics.
I-Spy for **15**

Crail
Close to Fife Ness, the old fishing village of Crail is the oldest Royal Borough in the East Neuk of Fife. It was granted its Royal Charter by Robert Bruce in 1310.
I-Spy for 15

Culross Palace
Some 7 miles west of Dunfermline, on the north shore of the River Forth stands Culross Palace. It was built in the seventeenth century on the site of an earlier palace. For what feature is the palace famous?

I-Spy for 15
Double with answer

Dunfermline Abbey
On the hill overlooking Dunfermline are the ruins of the abbey, which was founded in the eleventh century, and the remains of the royal palace. Who is buried in the choir of the abbey?

I-Spy for 20
Double with answer

Falkland Palace

Falkland Palace, some 6 miles to the north-east of Loch Leven, passed to the Stuarts in 1370. It contains the Royal Tennis Club of 1539, the oldest tennis club in Britain. When was much of the present palace built?

I-Spy for **20**— *double with answer*

St Andrews

The 'Royal and Ancient' Golf Club at St Andrews is known the world over as the home of golf. This is one of the four links courses there.

I-Spy for **20**

St Fillan's Cave

St Fillan's Cave is in Pittenweem, a coastal village where the Firth of Forth meets the North Sea, and overlooking the Isle of May. When was this holy shrine restored and rededicated?

I-Spy for **15** — *double with answer*

Edinburgh: Arthur's Seat
Looking down upon the fine old streets of Edinburgh (Scotland's capital since the sixteenth century) is the long-extinct volcano known as Arthur's Seat.
I-Spy for **15**

Edinburgh Castle
Edinburgh Castle is perched on a promontory of volcanic basalt rock some 90 metres (almost 300 ft) above the city. The oldest building here is the eleventh-century Chapel of St Margaret. The regalia of Scotland is housed in the castle.
I-Spy for **20**

Edinburgh: Gladstone's Land
Gladstone's Land, in Lawnmarket, Edinburgh is a tall, narrow, six-storey house built in 1620 and typical of its period. It is named after Thomas Gledstanes who bought the house just after it was built.
I-Spy for **15**

Edinburgh: Greyfriars Bobby

The little statue of Greyfriars Bobby, a Skye terrier, is to be seen in Greyfriars churchyard. After his master's death, the dog watched over the grave. For how long did the dog keep his vigil?

I-Spy for 25 — double with answer

Edinburgh: Greyfriars Church

Greyfriars Church was first opened in 1620 and rebuilt in 1721. It was built on the site of a fifteenth-century Franciscan friary.
I-Spy for 15

Edinburgh: Holyroodhouse

Holyroodhouse is the official residence of the Queen when she is in Scotland. The present palace dates from the seventeenth century. The 'Holy Rood' is a relic of the cross of Christ possessed by St Margaret of Scotland.
I-Spy for 20

Edinburgh: Huntly House

Huntly House in Canongate is a
sixteenth-century mansion which
houses today the collections of the
city's local history museum.
I-Spy for 20

Edinburgh: John Knox's House

The house stands in the Royal
Mile. John Knox (1513-72), the
fiery Scottish Protestant reformer,
founded the Church of
Scotland in 1560.
I-Spy for 20

Edinburgh: Sir Walter Scott Monument

Sir Walter Scott (1771-1832) went
to school and university in
Edinburgh, and this grand column
celebrates one of Scotland's most
famous writers. In which of his
books does Robin Hood appear?

I-Spy for 25 — double with answer

17

Forth Bridges

Two bridges span the Firth of Forth at Queensferry. The rail bridge (right) was completed in March 1890 and is a tribute to Victorian engineering. The road bridge (left) was opened by the Her Majesty the Queen. In which year?

I-Spy for 15 — double with answer

Hopetoun House

On the southern shore of the Firth of Forth, 3 miles west of Queensferry is Hopetoun House. Built in the eighteenth century, it resembles an English country mansion. It is still the home of the Hope family. The delightful grounds include a deer pa and wildlife centre.

I-Spy for 15

Lady Gifford's Well

About 20 miles south-west of Edinburgh
on the A702 lies the village of West
Linton, once famous for its stonemasons.
The statue on Lady Gifford's Well was
carved in 1666.
I-Spy for 20

Museum of Flight

The Museum of Flight at the former RAF
airfield at East Fortune to the east of
Edinburgh displays famous aircraft such
as a Spitfire and the last Comet 4.
I-Spy for 20

Preston Mill

The market town of East Linton
offers a sixteenth-century bridge
as well as Preston Mill, one of the
very few working water-mills
remaining in Scotland.
I-Spy for 20

Callander
The rugged mountains, tree-clad slopes, and lovely lochs of the Trossachs (meaning the 'bristly place') in Perthshire are visited by thousands of tourists every year. This was Rob Roy's favourite haunt. Not far away is the town of Callander where the Rob Roy Centre is to be found.
I-Spy for **20**

Falls of Dochart
Through the lovely village of Killin on the south-western tip of Loch Tay rush the waters over the Falls of Dochart. Members of the Clan McNab are buried on a tiny island on the River Dochart.
I-Spy for **25**

Loch Katrine
The steamer *Sir Walter Scott* plies its way through the sparkling waters of picturesque Loch Katrine in Scotland's Lake District, the Trossachs, some 10 miles to the west of Callander. Loch Katrine occupies a valley scoured out by the action of ice.
I-Spy for **15**

Ben Lomond

Beyond the quiet waters of Loch Lomond towers the hump of Ben Lomond. It is Scotland's most southerly mountain that reaches over 900 metres (3000 ft) in height. How high is it?

I-Spy for **20**
Double with answer

Loch Lomond

Studded with more than thirty islands and only a stone's throw north of Glasgow, Loch Lomond is Scotland's largest and most famous loch. How long is it?

I-Spy for **25**
Double with answer

Rob Roy's Grave

In the churchyard of Balquhidder, close to the ruined church, is the grave of one of Scotland's best-known folk heroes, Rob Roy (Gaelic *Red Robert*). He was born at Buchanan in Stirlingshire in 1671 and died at Balquhidder in 1734. What was Rob Roy's surname?

I-Spy for **20** *double with answer*

Stirling
Located on the River Forth between the Campsie Fells and the Ochil Hills, Stirling was once the proud capital of Scotland. Here is the Old Bridge. Nearby the Scottish knight, William Wallace (1272-1305), defeated the English in 1297.
I-Spy for **15**

Stirling Castle
Probably dating from the twelfth century, Stirling Castle was once the residence of the Scottish kings. The interior of the castle remains much as it was in the fourteenth century.
I-Spy for **20**

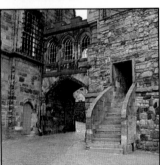

The Wallace Monument
The Wallace Monument at Abbey Craig, Stirling, honours the great Scottish patriot who eventually met his death at Smithfield in London by being hanged, drawn, and quartered.
I-Spy for **20**

Argyll Forest Park
Across the Firth of Clyde from Greenock is Dunoon and the Cowal Peninsula. Mountains, lochs, and no less than three forests make up the magnificent scenery of Argyll Forest Park
I-Spy for **15**

Ayr
Ayr is the county town of Ayrshire. Its charter dates from the early thirteenth century. It is popular with tourists because of its associations with Robert Burns, and this is his monument. Who, after the Civil War, had the Auld Kirk of Ayr built because the ancient church had been destroyed by his army?

I-Spy for **15**
Double with answer

Robert Burns' Birthplace
The poet Robert Burns (1759-96) was born in this thatched cottage at Alloway near Ayr. The cottage was built by his father, William Burns, a poor farmer.
I-Spy for **20**

Glasgow: Templeton's Carpet Factory

This former carpet factory is situated east of the People's Palace Museum in Glasgow Green. It was copied from a design for the Doge's Palace in Venice. Why is Glasgow Green famous?

I-Spy for 15
Double with answer

Glasgow: Royal Highland Fusiliers Museum

The exhibits in the Regimental Museum in Sauchiehall Street — Glasgow's most famous shopping street — are associated with four regiments.
I-Spy for 20

Glasgow: Provand's Lordship

Built in 1471, this is Glasgow's oldest house and one of only two medieval buildings in the city. It now houses a collection illustrating Scottish domestic life. Which is the other medieval building?

I-Spy for 15
Double with answer

Inveraray Bell Tower

The proud boast of Inveraray Bell Tower is that it houses the world's second-heaviest ring of ten bells which is also Scotland's finest. How high is the tower?

I-Spy for **20**
Double with answer

Mull of Kintyre

At some 40 miles in length, Kintyre is Scotland's longest peninsula. Only the Mull (Scottish for 'promontory') itself, with its wild moors and steep hills, serves as a reminder that this narrow finger of land is north of the Highland Boundary Fault.
I-Spy for **20**

Oban

Oban lies in a crescent-shaped hollow overlooking Oban Bay which is sheltered by the island of Kerrera. With its road, rail, and ferry links, Oban today is a popular holiday resort. It is regarded as the Gateway to the Isles.

I-Spy for 15

Oban: McCaig's Tower

Dominating the Oban skyline, the circular granite structure of McCaig's Tower was built by a local banker as a memorial to his family. Building work was abandoned in 1902 when John McCaig died

I-Spy for 20

Oban: St Columba's Cathedral

Gaelic-speaking Roman Catholics often worship in St Columba's Cathedral. Built entirely of granite, who designed it?

_____

_____

I-Spy for 15
Double with answer

Aberdeen
Known as the 'Granite City', Aberdeen seen here from the Balnagast Golf Course, retains its attractive old harbour area and other historic buildings. It has grown wealthy on North Sea oil.
*I-Spy for **15***

Aberdeen: King's College Chapel
King's College was founded by Bishop Elphinstone. The sixteenth-century chapel is very well known for its splendid woodwork. Its great 'crown' tower was built in the seventeenth century.
*I-Spy for **20***

Balmoral Castle
In the mid-nineteenth century Prince Albert bought the Balmoral estate, and a Baronial style castle was built as a royal residence in the Highlands for Queen Victoria and the Prince. The present castle was completed in 1855.
*I-Spy for **15***

Braemar Castle

Begun in 1628 by the Earl of Mar, Braemar Castle was largely destroyed in the Jacobite Rebellion of 1689. After the '45, it was rebuilt in 1748 as a garrison to subdue the Highlands. Which troops were stationed there?

I-Spy or **25** — *double with answer*

Braemar: R L Stevenson's House

Robert Louis Stevenson lived in this house on the Glenshee road in Braemar. It was here that, in 1881, he completed his famous book *Treasure Island*. What is the name of the young hero in his other well-known book *Kidnapped*?

I-Spy for **20**
Double with answer

Dufftown

Dufftown was founded in 1817 by the Earl of Fife, James Duff. This Clock Tower stands in the centre of the town. What does it contain?

I-Spy for 15
Double with answer

Dufftown: Glenfiddich Distillery

Dufftown is an important centre of the whisky distilling industry. The Glenfiddich Distillery, founded in the 1880s by the Grants, produces one of the world's best-known single malt whiskies.
I-Spy for 20

Grampian Transport Museum

The Grampian Transport Museum, in the village of Alford some 30 miles west of Aberdeen, is a great tourist attraction with its collection of vintage vehicles, including steam and horse-drawn machines.

I-Spy for 20

Sueno's Stone

The 23-foot (7-m) high Sueno's Stone in Forres is one of the most interesting sculpted stones in Scotland. It is an Ancient Monument and may be more than 1000 years old.

I-Spy for 15

West Buchan Railway

One of the many attractions that await young tourists in historic Banff is the narrow-gauge railway operated by steam and diesel locomotives. Banff was granted its Royal Charter in 1163.

I-Spy for 15

Aberfeldy

Aberfeldy is located on the A827 road and by the River Tay between Loch Tay and Pitlochry. It is a convenient centre for exploring the Grampian Mountains.

I-Spy for 15

Black Watch Monument

At Aberfeldy by General Wade's splendid five-arched bridge, built in 1733, is the Black Watch Monument. This famous regiment was first mustered in 1740. Why was it called the Black Watch?

I-Spy for 25 — double with answer _____

Pass of Killiekrankie

In 1689, Jacobite Highlanders routed the English troops in the wooded Killiekrankie gorge. The National Trust Visitor Centre exhibitions feature the battle.

I-Spy for 25

Ben Lawers

At 1215 metres (3984 ft), Ben Lawers — now owned by the National Trust for Scotland — towers over Loch Tay and, when the snows descend in winter, it is one of the Grampian Highlands' most magnificent mountains.

I-Spy for **20**

Glen Lyon

About 5 miles to the west of Aberfeldy, a turning left off the B846 takes the motorist on to a narrow road which runs for almost 20 miles through Glen Lyon and ending at Loch Lyon. With the giant Ben Lawers to the south, this is one of Scotland's 'classic' routes.

I-Spy for **25**

Moot Hill

Scone is about 3 miles north of Perth on the A93. Nearby is Scone Palace as well as Moot Hill which was the site of the stolen Stone of Destiny.

I-Spy for **25**

MOOT OR 'BOOT' HILL
Site of the coronations of the Kings of Scotland and of Scottish Parliaments. Artificial mound created by earth brought in the boots of men swearing loyalty to their King.

Perth

Until the middle of the fifteenth century, the Fair City of Perth, 'gateway to the Highlands', was the capital of Scotland. Without doubt, the finest view of the city is that from the summit of Kinnoull Hill.

I-Spy for **20**

Perth Bridge

Perth is an inland port on the River Tay. The old Perth Bridge was built in 1771. Of what was it built?

I-Spy for **15**
Double with answer

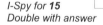

Pitlochry Salmon Ladder

Where the hydro-electric plant and dam have been constructed, the 300-metre (1000-ft) fish pass, including the Salmon Ladder, allow the migrating salmon to swim from pool to pool up the River Tay to their spawning grounds.

I-Spy for **15**

Soldier's Leap
After the Battle of Killiekrankie in 1689, a soldier of the defeated English army threw himself across the gorge and escaped from his pursuers.
I-Spy for 20

Tay Railway Bridge
This railway bridge spanning the River Tay was built to replace an earlier structure which was blown down. When was it built?

I-Spy for 25 — double with answer

Unicorn
In Victoria Dock in Dundee is the Frigate *Unicorn*. Now lacking her masts and sails, she is the oldest British-built warship afloat.
I-Spy for 20

34

Ardvreck Castle
Towards the eastern end of Loch Assynt by the A837 road to Lochinver stand the ruins of Ardvreck Castle, once the stronghold of the MacLeods of Assynt.

I-Spy for **15**

Cairngorms: Chairlift
The granite-cored mass of the Cairngorms is the biggest range of mountains over 1000 metres (3300 ft) in Britain. The Cairngorms have been popular with winter skiers since the 1960s.

I-Spy for **20**

Caledonian Canal
The Caledonian Canal was built by Thomas Telford (1757-1834) to carry nineteenth-century shipping from the North Sea to the Atlantic. Today, it offers pleasure boating and walking as here at Fort Augustus.

I-Spy for **15**

Glen Coe
Crossing Rannoch Moor in a north-westerly direction from Crianlarich on the A82 road, the often wet and desolate moorland gives way to the spectacular, wild, and brooding Glen Coe with its jagged rocks and high peaks on either side.
I-Spy for 15

Beinn Eighe
At 1009 metres (3309 ft), Beinn Eighe is a giant of the Torridon Highlands. The whole of its eastern section is a National Nature Reserve created in 1949 by the Nature Conservancy soon after it was set up.
I-Spy for 20

Fort George
North-east of Inverness stands the eighteenth-century Fort George, built after the '45 rising. It houses the Regimental Museum of the Seaforth and Cameron Highlanders.
I-Spy for 20

Eilean Donan Castle
On an islet at the meeting point of Lochs Duich, Alsh, and Long stands Eilean Donan Castle resembling the perfect Scottish stronghold. In fact it was built between 1912 and 1932 by Colonel John Macrae on the site of a thirteenth-century keep.
I-Spy for 15

Fort William

The first stronghold built on this site at the head of Loch Linnhe in 1655 was Inverlochy Castle. Next came Fort William named after William of Orange. This is the gate of the Old Fort which was destroyed in 1864 to make way for the railway.

I-Spy for **15**

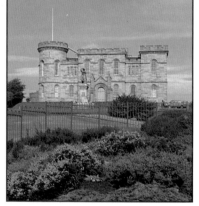

Inverness Castle

The glowing red sandstone walls of Inverness Castle overlook the right bank of the River Ness. Victorian rather than medieval, it was built between 1834 and 1837 as a Sheriff Court and jail. Flora Macdonald's statue stands outside.

I-Spy for **15**

Inverness: St Andrew's Cathedral

Overlooking the River Ness, the Cathedral at Inverness has a splendid interior. Despite its Gothic style, it was built between 1866 and 1869.

I-Spy for **15**

Inverness: Town House

Inverness is often described as the capital of the Highlands. The typically Scottish Victorian Town House was built in 1878. When did the British Cabinet meet here to discuss the Irish Treaty?

I-Spy for 15
Double with answer

Loch Linnhe

Loch Linnhe is linked to the sea by the Firth of Lorn, and this long arm of water follows the line of the Great Glen Fault separating the Grampians from the Western and Northern Highlands.
I-Spy for 15

Loch Ness

Another of the Great Glen lochs, Ness is some 24 miles long and more than a mile wide. Tales of its monster have captured the imagination since St Columba claimed to have seen it in the sixth century.
I-Spy for 15

Ben Nevis
At 1343 metres (4406 ft), the great granitic and volcanic bulk of Ben Nevis is the highest mountain in the British Isles, but it is only from the north-west that its magnificence can be appreciated.
I-Spy for 15

Loch Torridon
Loch Torridon is a sea loch offering great contrast in scenery on its southern and northern shores. Looking to the north, here is Beinn Alligin rising to a height of 985 metres (3232 ft).
I-Spy for 20

Urquhart Castle
Urquhart Castle on the shores of Loch Ness occupies a site that has probably been fortified since the Iron Age. The present structure was built between the fourteenth and sixteenth centuries.
I-Spy for 15

Including the Hebrides and the Clyde islands, there are some twenty-three islands off the west coast of Scotland which are served by the area's principal ferry operator. Including some which are little more than rocks, however, there are more than 200 islands in the archipelago which makes up the Hebrides alone. Thus, there is no space here to do more than show a small number of the islands and their features but you also have the chance to score I-Spy points by spotting islands and places which are not pictured.

I-Spy 20 for each of the following:

Isle of Arran: Glen Rosa ☐

Isle of Arran: Goat Fell ☐

Barra: Castlebay ☐

Bute: Rothesay ☐

Coll ☐

Colonsay: Fingal's Limpet Hammers ☐

Cumbraes ☐

Gigha ☐

Harris: St Clement's Church, Rodel ☐

Iona: St Mary's Abbey ☐

Islay: Kilnave Chapel ☐

Jura: The Paps ☐

Isle of Lewis: Callanish Standing Stones ☐

Lismore ☐

Mull: Ben More ☐

Raasay ☐

Rum, Eigg, Muck, and Canna ☐ ☐ ☐ ☐

Scalpay ☐

Isle of Skye: Armadale Castle ☐

Tiree ☐

North and South Uist ☐ ☐

Isle of Arran: Brodick Castle

The present castle is mainly of nineteenth-century construction although there was probably a fortification on this site close to Arran's principal village since the twelfth century.

I-Spy for 15 ☐

Iona: MacLean's Cross

This is MacLean's Cross on the tiny island of Iona off the south-western tip of Mull. After the Reformation, the island was seized by the MacLeans of Duart. Which famous saint made Iona his home?

I-Spy for 15 Double with answer ☐

Mull

Mull is the third largest island in the Hebrides and lies to the west of Oban. The mainly eighteenth-century harbour village of Tobermory, with its colourfully painted houses, offers a good range of tourist facilities.
I-Spy for **15**

Rum

Rum (pronounced 'room') is the largest island of the group which includes Eigg and Muck and which are situated to the south of Skye. It has a resident population of only forty people who work mainly for the Nature Conservancy who manage the island as an outdoor natural laboratory.
I-Spy for **20**

Isle of Skye: Cottage Museum

The Skye Cottage Museum at Kilmuir, some 20 miles north-north-west of Portree is based around four restored black houses which contain various exhibits explaining traditional island life.
I-Spy for **20**

Isle of Skye: Cuillin Hills
This spectacular winter scene of the Cuillin Hills was taken from
Sligachan, an angling resort on the Isle of Skye.
I-Spy for **20**

**Isle of Skye:
Dunvegan Castle**
Dunvegan Castle has
been the ancestral
home of the chiefs of
the MacLeod clan
since the thirteenth
century. It is open to
the public and
contains a fascinating
display of MacLeod
relics.
I-Spy for **20**

Isle of Skye: Lochalsh

Kyleakin will be the view that anyone making their first crossing by the ferry from the Kyle of Lochalsh will have of the 'isle of mist'. The passage takes just five minutes and the arrival is a little disappointing but the rest of the island more than makes up for it.
I-Spy for **20**

Isle of Skye: The Quiraing

On the northernmost peninsula of Skye, Trotternish, is the extraordinary maze of fallen blocks of rock known as the Quiraing. It has resulted from land slips and faults which took place thousands of years ago.
I-Spy for **20**

Isle of Skye: The Storr

The precipitous inland cliff of the Storr at over 718 metres (2358 ft) dominates the coast road to Trotternish from Portree. In front of it is the pinnacle of rock known as the Old Man of Storr.
I-Spy for **20**

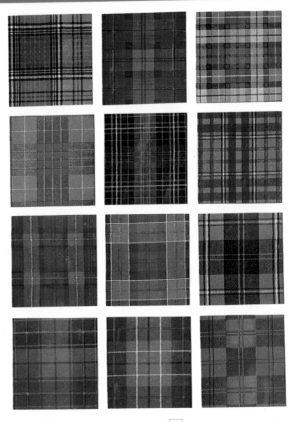

1	2	3
4	5	6
7	8	9
10	11	12

1 Anderson

2 Armstrong

3 Buchanan

4 Cameron

5 Cameron of Erracht

6 Cameron of Lochiel

7 Campbell of Argyll

8 Colquhoun

9 Cunningham

10 Davidson

11 Duncan

12 Erskine

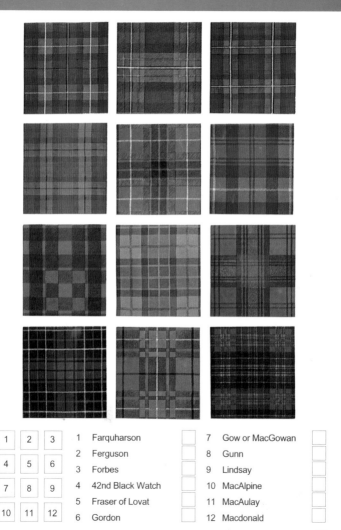

1	2	3
4	5	6
7	8	9
10	11	12

1	Farquharson		7	Gow or MacGowan	
2	Ferguson		8	Gunn	
3	Forbes		9	Lindsay	
4	42nd Black Watch		10	MacAlpine	
5	Fraser of Lovat		11	MacAulay	
6	Gordon		12	Macdonald	

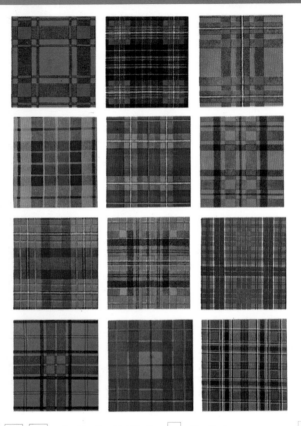

1	2	3
4	5	6
7	8	9
10	11	12

1 Macdonald of Sleat ☐
2 Macdonell of Glengarry ☐
3 Macgregor ☐
4 Mackay ☐
5 Mackenzie ☐
6 Macintosh ☐

7 Maclaren ☐
8 Macpherson ☐
9 Macrae ☐
10 Maxwell ☐
11 Morrison ☐
12 Munro ☐

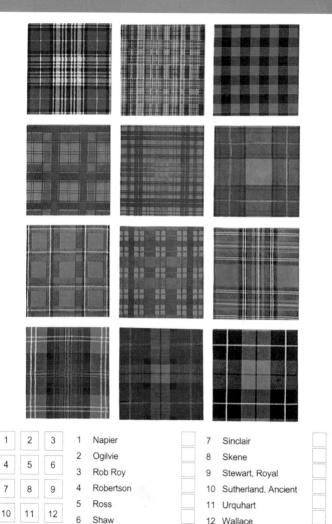

INDEX

Answers

Burns' Statue: 1791.
Thomas Carlyle's Birthplace: His father and uncle.
Craigleith Collection: China, Japan, and America.
Kirkcudbright: Leonard Robertson, a burgess of Ayr; Oliver Cromwell in 1664.
Museum of Costume: Leith.
Maxwelton House: 1682.
Abbotsford House: Clarity Hole — a dirty place.
Abbotsford's Gardens: His gun.
Edin's Hall Broch: A Pictish fort.
Curious Palace: its magnificent painted ceilings.
Dunfermline Abbey: Robert Bruce.
Falkland Palace: 1501-41.
St Fillan's Cave: 1935.
Edinburgh: Greyfriars Bobby: 14 years.
Scott Monument.

Glasgow: Templeton's Carpet Factory: it is the oldest public park in Britain.
Glasgow Cathedral: Provand's Lordship.
Inveraray Bell Tower: 38.4 metres (126 ft).
Oban: St Columba's Cathedral: Sir Giles Scott.
Braemar Castle: Hanoverian Troops.
Braemar: R L Stevenson's House: David Balfour.
Dufftown: A social history museum.
Black Watch Monument: Because of its dark tartan.
Perth Bridge: rose-red sandstone.
Tay Railway Bridge: 1879.
Inverness: Town House: 1921.
Iona, Mac Lean's Cross: St Columba.

© I-Spy Limited 1993

ISBN (paperback) 1 85671 129 3

Michelin Tyre Public Limited Company
Davy House, Lyon Road, Harrow, Middlesex HA1 2DQ

MICHELIN and the Michelin Man are Registered Trademarks of Michelin

Edited and designed by Curtis Garratt Limited, The Old Vicarage, Horton cum Studley, Oxford OX9 1BT

The Publisher gratefully acknowledges the contribution of AA Picture/Photo Library who provided the majority of the photographs in this I-Spy book. Additional photographs by James Davis Travel Photography and Tom Hand. Most of the tartans shown are by courtesy of Duncan Chisholm & Son of Inverness. The Publisher also wishes to acknowledge Martspress Limited who assembled the majority of the photographs and provided information from which the text was written.

Colour reproduction by Anglia Colour Limited.

Printed in Spain.